Ter Actors

Thumb-bold,
Thibity-thold,
Langman,
Lick pan,
Mammie's wee man.

Collected by Pamela Lloyd
Illustrated by Mary Davy

RIGBY

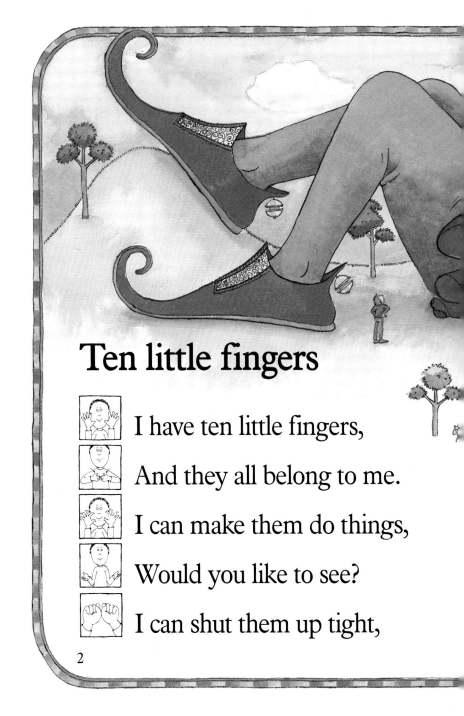

Ten little fingers

I have ten little fingers,

And they all belong to me.

I can make them do things,

Would you like to see?

I can shut them up tight,

 Or open them all wide.

Put them all together,

 Or make them jump high.

 I can make them jump low,

I can fold them quietly,

And hold them just so.

Snail

Snail, snail, come out of your hole,

Inside your shell it's black as coal.

Snail, snail put out your horns,

I'll give you bread and barley corn

Two little monkeys

Two little monkeys fighting in bed.

One fell out and hurt his head.

The other called the doctor,

And the doctor said,

"That's what you get

For fighting in bed!"

The cherry tree

Once I found a cherry stone,

I put it on the ground,

And when I came to look at it,

A tiny shoot I found.

The shoot grew up and up each da

And soon became a tree.

I picked the rosy cherries then,

And ate them for my tea.

Stir-about

 Into the basin put the plums,

 Stir-about, stir-about, stir-about.

 Next the good white flour comes,

 Stir-about, stir-about, stir-about.

 Sugar and peel and eggs and spice,

 Stir-about, stir-about, stir-about.

 Mix them and fix them

 And cook them twice,

 Stir-about, stir-about, stir-about!

7

Five little babies

One little baby

Rocking in a tree.

Two little babies

Splashing in the sea.

Three little babies

Crawling on the floor.

8

 Four little babies

 Banging on the door.

 Five little babies

 Playing hide and seek.

Keep your eyes closed tight, now,

 Until I say . . . PEEK!

9

The caterpillar

 A caterpillar crawled

To the top of a tree.

"I think I'll take a nap," said he.

So – under a leaf he began to creep

To spin a cocoon,

Then he fell asleep.

All winter he slept in his cocoon bed,

Till spring came along

one day and said,

"Wake up, wake up, sleepyhead."

So – he opened his eyes

That sunshiny day.

Lo! He was a butterfly –

And flew away!

Five little kittens

Five little kittens

Sleeping on a chair,

One rolled off,

Leaving four there.

Four little kittens,

One climbed a tree

To look in a bird's nest,

Then there were three.

Three little kittens

Wondered what to do,

 One saw a mouse,

 Then there were two.

 Two little kittens

Playing near a wall,

 One little kitten

 Chased a red ball.

 One little kitten

 With fur soft as silk,

Left all alone

 To drink a dish of milk.

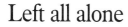

Farmer Giles

 Here sits Farmer Giles,

 Here sit his two men,

 Here sits the cockadoodle,

Here sits the hen.

Here sit the little chickens,

Here they run in,

Chin chopper, chin chopper,

Chin, chin, chin.

Two fat gentlemen

Two fat gentlemen met in a lane,

Bowed most politely,

bowed once again.

How do you do? How do you do?

How do you do again?

Two thin ladies met in a lane,

etc . . .

Two tall policemen met in a lane,

etc . . .

Two little schoolboys met in a lane,

etc . . .

Two little babies met in a lane,

etc . . .

17

Washing linen

 We are washing linen, linen,

 We are washing linen clean.

We are rinsing linen, linen,

We are rinsing linen clean.

 We are wringing linen, linen,

We are wringing linen clean.

 We are hanging linen, linen,

We are hanging linen clean.

 We are wearing linen, linen,

We are wearing linen clean.

19

Little cottage

 Little cottage in a wood.

 Little man at a window stood.

 Saw a rabbit running by,

 Knocking at the door.

"Help me! Help me!

Help!" he cried,

"See the hunters on their way."

"Little rabbit, come inside,

You'll be safe with me."

21

The turtle

 There was a little turtle,

 He lived in a box.

 He swam in a puddle,

He climbed on the rocks.

He snapped at a mosquito,

He snapped at a flea.

He snapped at a minnow,

He snapped at me.

He caught the mosquito,

He caught the flea.

He caught the minnow,

But he didn't catch me!

The President's tea

O Pillykin, Willykin, Winky, Wee,

How does the President

take his tea?

He takes it with melons,

He takes it with milk,

He takes it with syrup

And sassafras silk.

He takes it without,

He takes it within –

O Punky-doodle

and Jollapin!